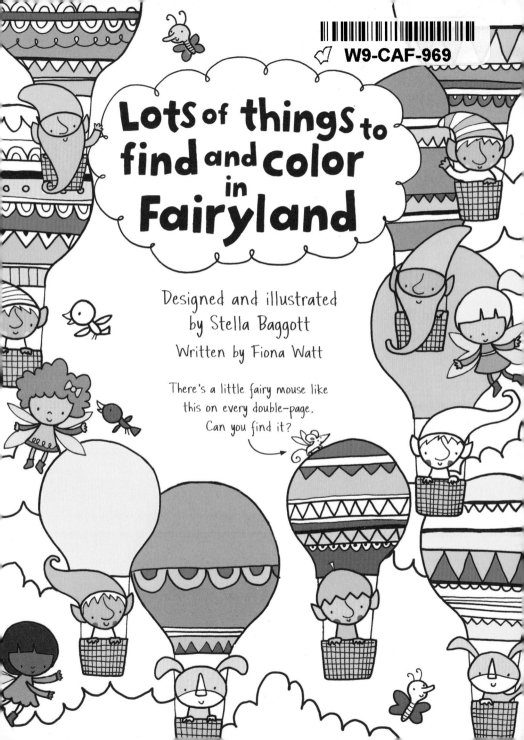

Lots of things to find and color in Fairyland

Designed and illustrated
by Stella Baggott

Written by Fiona Watt

There's a little fairy mouse like
this on every double-page.
Can you find it?

Find all the fairies with bows in their hair and color them in.

Can you spot a fairy wearing a spotted dress?

2

Find the squirrels and color them orange.

Look for the fairy wearing a headband and color it yellow.

Add pretty patterns to the plain dresses.

3

Find the toadstools
with two windows
and color these
toadstools red.

Can you spot a
butterfly? Color
it in when you
find it.

4

Find and color all the bees yellow.

Look for the houses with gnomes in the windows and color them in.

5

Find all the flowers with white faces and color them.

Can you spot five sleeping flowers?

Here's a pink fairy. Find five more.

6

This snail has a spiral on its shell. Find more snails and give them spirals too.

Find the butterflies with white wings and color them blue.

Can you spot seven butterflies with pink wings?

7

Find the gnomes carrying two acorns and color their hats red.

Can you spot the gnome with no acorn?

Find the gnomes carrying one acorn and color their hats green.

8

Spot the elf hiding among the toadstools and color his hat red.

Draw spots on all the plain toadstools.

Find the toadstools with snails on top and color in their shells.

9

Can you spot a fairy mouse holding a cupcake? Color her wings yellow.

Find the fairy mice holding wands and color their dresses and wings pink.

10

Look for the fairy mice wearing crowns and color their dresses blue.

Find all the fairies and color their dresses yellow.

Can you spot a fairy who has lost her hat? Color her wings pink.

Look for the bugs and color them orange.

13

Find the elves with two bugs in their jars and color in the elves.

Can you spot four elves with a caterpillar in their jars?

14

Look for an elf who has caught a butterfly in his net and color him in.

Find the bees and color them yellow.

Find all the sleeping acorns and color them green.

Can you spot the acorn wearing a hat?

16

Color in
the snails.

Follow the trail to find
out which snail has
been eating the flower.

Find another flower the same as this and color it to match.

Find the fairies hiding among the leaves and color them in.

18

Color all the
flowers in pinks
and purples.

19

Find and color all the fairies with flowers in their hair.

Look for the birds and color them blue, and color all the suns yellow.

Can you spot the butterfly with hearts on its wings?

21

Can you find the fairy hiding in the flowers?

Can you spot five bees?

Spot five pink butterflies.

22